TAKING MY PEN FOR A WALK

TAKING MY PEN FOR A WALK

Julie O'Callaghan

ORCHARD BOOKS
London and New York

ACKNOWLEDGMENTS:
The Times Literary Supplement, The Irish Times,
Bright Lights Blaze Out (Oxford University Press, 1986)

A bursary from the Irish Arts Council/An Chomhairle
Ealaíon assisted the completion of this book

First published in Great Britain in 1988 by
ORCHARD BOOKS
10 Golden Square, London W1R 3AF
Orchard Books Canada
20 Torbay Road, Markham Ontario 23P 1G6
Orchard Books Australia
14 Mars Road, Lane Cove NSW 2006
1 85213 109 8
Printed in Great Britain by A. Wheaton & Co. Ltd, Exeter

for Dennis

Contents

Taking My Pen for a Walk

Tonight I took the leash off my pen.
At first it was frightened,
looked up at me with confused eyes, tongue panting.
Then I said, 'Go on, run away,'
and pushed its head.
Still it wasn't sure what I wanted;
it whimpered with its tail between its legs.
So I yelled, 'You're free, why don't you run —
you stupid pen, you should be glad.
Now get out of my sight.'
It took a few steps.
I stamped my foot and threw a stone.
Suddenly, it realised what I was saying
and began to run furiously away from me.

My Hat

Straight up
above my head
sits my spectacular
hat of air.
Maybe today
for decoration
I'll wear
a feathery cloud
to attract attention.
The wind never
blows my hat off
but sometimes
my head is tired
of such a fine high hat.

Happy Birthday from Bennigans

Why did you do it, Mother?
I told you — didn't I — that I'd go with you
to a restaurant for my birthday
on one condition: Don't go and blab
to the waitress it's my BIG DAY.
But you had to go and tell her.
God, what if somebody had seen me?
I realise that you and Daddy
simply do not care if you ruin my reputation.
I almost thought for a teensy second
you had restrained yourself for once.
But no. You and your big mouth.
'Hip, hop, happy, b, birth, day,
hap, hap, happy, Happy Birthday to You!':
a zero girl, singing a zero song
at the top of her nothingness of a voice.
'All of us at Bennigans hope it's a special day!'
All of them, Mother, not just some.
That's IT for birthdays from now on.
Next year I'll be celebrating by myself.

17

Crunching Home from School

a paper my mother has to sign in my mitten
kick a toe-full of snow at you
get one in the mouth
my knitted winter cap:
green, red, blue, yellow
hanging with a tassel down my back
pack a snowball, hide, throw it,
run, slip into a hill of snow
that car is stuck
the lady spinning her wheels
and looking angry
'hey do you want a push?'
then clap as she honks and drives away
squirting snow on our coats from her tyres
snow down the boot best form of torture
who can slide on ice the longest

boys hide behind parked cars
waiting for a truck with big bumpers
so they can grab onto them
and skim down the street
here comes one
they crouch for the kill
snow blinding everyone
they've got the bumper
truck stops
reverses
they are foiled
I hand my mother a soggy notice

High Life

My home is on the eighty-ninth floor.
I live above the storms.

My windows are the cockpit
of an airplane that never flies.

The builders thought they were smart
but the wind is smarter

and I grow dizzy and weak
as I watch the water in my sink

flop back and forth
as we blow to and fro.

I grab the towel rack
to steady myself.

A wispy cloud
crashes through my livingroom wall.

I scream over the phone
'what's the weather like down there?'

I'm Sorry . . . .

I'm sorry
but nobody knows me like that music
I don't pretend to
know myself as well.

It knows what I feel.
It knows what I like to hear.
It is wise enough to end
at the moment before I yawn
and say let's hear a new tune.

I sure wish I knew someone
like that symphonyfolkrock
crazy thing
knows me.

Grown Up

Bored by the day,
I decided I'd do something
I hadn't done in years —
go outside and play.
I tried to remember
jump rope games,
the rules of hide and seek,
did you count to forty or a hundred?

I went out and attempted to act naturally.
I hummed a little and kicked a stone
down the street looking for other kids.
They were playing hopscotch.
I showed them marbles
and penny candy and dominoes.
They stared up at me like lilliputians
and said I was too old.

Show Biz

I walk down a Hollywood street
Of New York
There goes Gene Kelly
He turns and says
Pardon me, haven't I seen you somewhere before?
I pretend I don't hear and brush by
He grabs my arm and sings a song about
Don't be afraid it's just me
And the lights of Broadway flare up
As Gene and I go into our boy meets girl number
A few jumps, then a turn and a lift
Now an arabesque
He says *gee you're terrif*
Would you like to star in my new show?
Me? I say I've never been in a show before
Trust me is his next line — *I'll make you a star*
My mean aunt hears of my up-and-coming career
And sends me off to Europe
I cry on the boat all the way there
Gene follows me and brings me back
The billboard glows my name in lights

Swan Lake

Tonight, when all the other girls rush
to the station or bus stop to get home fast
for a T.V. dinner and television,
I won't be in a hurry.

I'll casually cross the street to McDonald's
and while eating I'll imagine
what it's like after the overture
as the curtain goes up on Swan Lake.

I bought the second-most expensive ticket
on my lunch-break. I don't know how
I can wait two-and-a-half more hours until I get out.
It was just a whim — I was bored with the same old rout

The girls thought I had a big date when they saw me.
I told them I was going to the ballet.
The palaces, princes and magic forest
will be waiting for me to finish my hamburger.

At the Science and Industry Museum

I'm not joking ya,
there was a gigantic ear
with this place to walk through
just like a cave with an eardrum
beating all around you.
In the middle was a slide show
where this guy was talking about ears,
telling us to look at different parts
and he'd tell us what they were.
On the other side of the tunnel
that went through the gigantic ear
was a huge chamber you could go in
and there were some more slide shows
and kids messing around inside this heart
until their teacher told them to cut it out.
She told them they better watch the slide show
'cause she was gonna have a quiz on what they learned.
When ya come out of the heart ya see
lots of old planes hanging from the ceiling
until ya come to this place where ya press a button
that makes a little classroom light up
with a bunch of puppets singing.
Once in a while they'd move their heads
or their wooden mouths'd go up and down
to look like singing. It was all about
electricity and telephones and stuff like that.

25

I forget some of the things I saw
'cause everywhere ya went ya had to keep
pressing buttons and listening to men on telephones
explaining factories and how steel is made
and how to know different minerals.
Sometimes I'd press two buttons at once
and pick up two different telephones
and watch while a fake flower was growing
or a machine was drilling for oil
or a guy was making something.
But then Miss Freytag came by and I got yelled at.
There was a big farm that looked like the movies.
You could walk through a real farmhouse,
see a tractor and combine harvester
and watch a few eggs with chickens pecking out.
They had the walls painted with trees and fences
so you'd think you were outside.

In this other exhibit was a washing machine
that went up to the ceiling and was made of plastic
so you could see all the socks and shirts
and underwear going around in it.
If you stay watching the clothes long enough
you get a free ride around the room
'cause the floor goes in circles.
My favourite place was the echo chamber
where you stand at one end of this long room
and somebody else stands at the other side
and even if you whisper the other guy can hear ya.
I think it must've been a trick.
Other things I saw were the babies in jars,
the coal mine, the picture telephone, a space capsule
and millions of other slide shows and movies.
I hope we can go there again
'cause it's funner than school.

Bo-Peep

My red cape is a skirt
my cousin left us last year
since she gained so much weight
she couldn't fit into it anymore.
The lacy petticoat
under my flouncy dress
is a ripped curtain
my mother was going to throw out
until I grabbed it and said,
'You never know what you can do
with stuff like that.'
My golden braid, hanging to my butt,
is a ball of wool
I was supposed to be making a cardigan
for my sister with.
She said she didn't mind waiting
a little longer.
My shepherd's staff is a golf club
with five hangers covered in pretty paper.
For shoe-buckles, I cut up some
Chinese take-away containers.
To top it all, I'm wearing my best friend's shower cap
with a plastic flower sticking out from the elastic —
how do I look?

Me

I have driven myself to a party.
I am at it right now.
Something stringy like thread,
but in big bunches, is hanging
off the top of my head.
I can see it out of the corner of a gooey globe
located somewhere in my face.
How odd that my toes are tied
into pieces off a cow's back!
I see them resting way down on a board
cut from a Norwegian forest.
Before I came I put on a skirt, a blouse
and some kind of fleecy thing
that I robbed from a sheep.
My finger wears a shiny doughnut
from a cave far away from here.
I told my Indian skirt to stop bickering
with my American slip.

Sparks were flying, they were crackling
and rustling so much that I couldn't hear
what those two wormy lips,
guarding a pit with ivory, said.
The backs of my hands have see-through flesh on them
with blue bulges pulsing.
I always try to hide them
when I'm in company.
I seem also to have two growths
of a rather grotesque nature
on either side of my creaking jaws.
These I decorate with beads to camouflage them.
At least no one has noticed them yet.

My Trusty Fingers

My fingers haven't worn out yet
and they are five thousand days old.
They're still bending at all the right
joints and knuckles
and I'm very proud of them.
They automatically scratch my chin if it tickles
and today they handed up
the bus fare without me even opening my mouth.
They are writing this thing just now
even though (between ourselves) I happen to know
they want to be knitting a sweater.
They really should be celebrities.

My Dad

I love to watch my dad
when he's cutting his toenails.
My dad does not mind
if he has an audience.
He is like a medical T.V. show
during a tricky operation.
He says, 'First you trim the nail
leaving a strip of white at the top
before probing under the nail for crud.'
The crud is all different colours
because it is fluff from his socks.
He cannot understand people
who think that's all there is
to cutting your nails.
Neither can I.
Next he wedges a tiny pair of silver scissors
into the corner and takes another scissors
and goes clip, clip, clip.
That's for ingrown toenails.
To polish things off,
he scrapes the sides of his nail
with a little file just in case.
I would like to be as skilled
as my dad at cutting toenails
in the years to come.

Putting Down the Time

the tar on the street
is melted now

we leave footprints
our back door squeaks

we stopped complaining
about the heat

the bottoms of our feet
have turned leathery

down to the store
demolish an ice cream

back to the beach
the water's too cold

over to a friend's
slurping a watermelon

beside a baked automobile
calling out the next game

33

Flute

Sitting in Her Majesty's apartment
one evening, I heard a flute outside
and listened as though the music
were for my ears only.

When it stopped playing the Empress said,
'That flute was like the autumn wind.
Why did you make no answering sound?'
The ladies around her giggled at me.

I replied, 'It was the flute's fault,
for it passed too soon
and did not wait for my response.'
'Splendid,' the Empress smiled,
'that's precisely what you should have said.'

The Royal Hair

The Empress is five feet tall
her hair is six feet long
and trails behind her
in processions.

Every morning
I clean out her combs
and prepare perfumed oils
to dress her black strands.

Today she sits on a silk cushion
watching the snow fall.
Her voice is weak — her hair is damp
and I can tell she is drowning in a sea of tears.

The tangles and knots
are as thick as a jungle
but I don't mind — my hair
is twice as fine and shiny.

The Beach Trail

That was the most tedious journey
ever travelled, the most torturous trail
known to mankind:
at five thirty on a summer evening
with our gritty teeth,
our smelly towels,
with our buckets of rare stones
and shoes full of shells never before seen,
with our ears full of sand,
our skin burning,
our hair decorated with seaweed,
with a piece of glass in our heel,
our mother's radio,
our cousin's beachball,

with an ice cream bar in our stomachs,
a special hunk of driftwood,
an arm, neck and leg full of mosquito bites,
our bathing suits damp and itchy,
with out tempers frayed,
our gym shoes lost,
our money spent,
our holes dug,
our castles wrecked,
our sand battles won,
we paraded down the street
and back to civilization
as we knew it.

Saturday

among the synthetic shoes
at Woolworths
Saturday
of the dirty snow
in parking lots
Saturday
with the piano pounding
during ballet class
Saturday
between two Walt Disney movies
coming attractions
Saturday
sitting in the car
fighting
Saturday
Fred's Finer Foods
Horton's Hardware
Saturday
Spotless Cleaners
Swanky Modes
Saturday

Indians

They stayed for a week or two
in an arrow-shaped teepee
wearing bargain-shop beads and moccasins.

They washed their clothes in a pond
of inflatable plastic — the water
came from a garden hose.

Some nights they gathered around a bonfire
of leaves and newspaper, cooking potatoes
in aluminium foil.

When things became dull, they plugged in
a portable television set and watched
pale-face acting the clown.

The braves wore cheap lipstick and eyeshadow
as warpaint and a feathery headdress
someone gave them at Christmas.

The squaws got sick of eating berries,
carrying blonde dolls as their papoose
and went indoors to play house.

Advice on a Winter Beach

The beach
is bleak in winter;
monsters made of ice,
the green rolling waves
frozen stiff and white.

Children sometimes
break through into a world
of hibernating fish and angels.
The frost-wind will freeze
your red-red blood.

Pinch your ear lobes,
rub your hands,
stamp your feet,
turn home before the icicles
form on your nose.

Battle

We knew it would come all day —
nervously we checked the windows
and tried to imagine what we'd do
once it was here.

The announcement came about four.
They told us to get home as best we could.
The only escape was through the battle itself.
Collars up, hats pulled down,

we forced the front doors open
on the howling, ruthless enemy outside.
Most of us were headed for underground bunkers
where trains had been arranged secretly

to evacuate our citizens quickly.
The casualties were numerous —
people fell on all sides of me.
Everyone was sure they'd never see home again.

Packed inside the bunkers — no one spoke
waiting for transport, thinking of families
and warm houses — while above us
invaders ransacked our streets,

desecrated our monuments and whooped it up.
We were captured, but it happened every year,
and none of us raised a hand to the enemy.
At the end of our journey were shovels and revenge.

Hedgehog's Classroom

The Grey Kitten sits at the front
with a dunce-hat on her head.
Squirrel fires a spit-ball
from the fourth row back
which misses Ferret's head by a millimetre.
Rat is rooting in his desk
for the last piece of cheese he has stashed
and the Calico Kitten is twitching
his whiskers and flapping his ears,
trying to make the dunce laugh.
Hedgehog looks through his glasses,
past his class notes, and waves
his wooden pointer as a threat:
'Rat, please stand up and explain
to us what you have in your desk
that has kept your attention
from my lesson for ten solid minutes.'
With this diversion, Ferret passes a note
to Black Kitten which says,
'Are you going hunting after school?
If so, can I come with you, please say yes.'
The Black Kitten's mouth forms one word: 'No.'
The wooden pointer arrives at his face:
'Ferret and Black Kitten one hundred times for tomorrow —
I will not pass notes in class.'

The Wendella Boat Ride

We ride the school bus first
down the outer-drive, singing songs.
(Thank you mister bus-driver)
At the river we see the boat,
a little man waits beside it.
He is the captain and by now
(we take this boat-ride every year)
he recognises us and shakes the fat hand
of the nun who teaches us.
We walk across a plank down to the boat
jingling coins in our pockets.
Can I have two bags of popcorn, please,
and a purple lollipop that says, 'Welcome to Chicago'?
The other passengers are foreigners from Kentucky
with crew-cuts and funny-sounding phrases like
y'all and *these here* and *dang it all.*

Up the river for ten minutes, turn,
down the river to the locks,
through the locks to the lake,
across the harbour for breathtaking views of the skyline,
back again through the locks:
Thanks for coming, enjoy your visit to the 'I Will' city.

Sister, Sister, the I will what city?
The I-will-behave-myself city.

In the Park

Every breath tasted of roses.
Palm trees shaded our path
along a running brook.
We came to a glade
where flowers grew above our heads
and bent down for us to smell them.
The air was moist as a fern.
Children threw pennies into a lily pond.
A cockatoo flew from branch to branch.
I pointed my finger to a rare bloom
and a rainbow finch took it for a perch.
A squirrel monkey swung from my arm
eating a marshmallow upside down.
The venus fly-trap tried to grab my hand;
but I will miss most a shy plant
that folded all its leaves
when I stroked it goodbye.

Light the Lights

'Third grade Chinese women, next please!'
We came shuffling out of the stage wings,
squinting at the footlights, holding umbrellas.
Mrs. Fox arranged us by tugging our arms;
then she'd point to the pianist dramatically
and say, 'From the top, Mrs. Henderson,
if you please', and start to dance.
'Remember you're Chinese, O.K.?
They aren't clod-hoppers in China,
so when you make your entrance
I want little teensy steps, like so.'
She bowed her head, holding her umbrella
up high and tip-toed in.
'Now, when Mrs. Henderson hits these chords,
hold your umbrellas in front of you
and twirl two-three-four, five-six-seven-eight.
Then step-curtsy, step-curtsy,
shuffle-step, shuffle-step, to the right:
twirl two-three-four, to the left: two-three-four.
This is where we come to the tricky part.

We really have to be careful here
and don't be clumsy: put your umbrellas
over your left shoulder and follow the person
in front of you, until your toes
are on this line which forms a circle.
I'll give each of you a number
and I want even-numbered umbrellas
to tilt them outside two-three-four
and odd-numbered umbrellas inside two-three-four;
then switch two-three-four
odd on the outside, even on the inside.
Arabesque two-three-four, five-six-seven-eight
with your umbrellas over your heads
and then bow two-three-four
and that's the first half. All right.
Now original positions:
AND twirl two-three-four.
Stop! I want a twirl, not a stab! O.K.?
Again please, Mrs. Henderson.'

Country Cousins

They look down the track
waiting for a noise.
The humid conservatory
of back lanes and fields
seems so boring to them
while thinking of the city
with buildings and suburbs
that they stamp their feet with impatience,
lean over and peer.
Their father paces back and forth
throwing useless cautions to them
and pushes more hair
over his bald spot.

TMPW—D

Frying Tonight

This chip shop lady
has a certain way about her:
a way of saying — 'You O.K.?',
a way of making a wire basket
full of chips bounce up and down
with one hand while the other
flips back her hair,
a way of snapping up a chip bag,
flicking it with two fingers to open it
and pushing her fist in it to keep it open,
a way of setting out all the orders
in a neat row, of smoothing down her apron
to rid her hands of grease,
a way of making you notice
an extraordinary shade of blue
on her upper eyelid
as she bats her lashes and says, 'Is that everything, lov

Sister in a Whale

You live in the hollow of a stranded whale
lying on top of our house.
My father was embarrassed by this
so a roof was put up as camouflage.
On the ribs you have hung plants
and a miniature replica of a whale
to remind you where you are.
The stomach lining is plastered with posters
and your Snoopy for President buttons
are stuck to a piece of blubber beside your bed.
Through the spout you observe cloud formations.
It isn't as orderly as a regular room:
it's more like a shipwreck of notebooks,
school projects, shirts, paper bags,
coke cans, photographs and magazines
that has been washed up with the tide.
You beachcomb every morning for something to wear;
then it's down the corkscrew
to the real world.

Birthday Party

Aiming clothespins at the mouths of jars
or tails at the rear-ends of donkeys
made twelve pairs of patent leather pumps
want to run into the dining-room
where a cake and paper cups full of candy waited.
To help digestion they watched
a Fred Flintstone cartoon on the wall.
The party girl's fingers itched
for the pile of presents.
Open your presents now!
That's what the ones who knew
a thing or two about a party would say
just before they'd ask for another piece of cake.
The girls settled their skirts in a ring
and clapped at cologne, coloured markers
or a comb and brush set being unwrapped.
I wish I had one of them.
If all the presents were open
some spoil-sport father
would ring the door bell.
Hurry up, pumpkin, I'm double-parked.
The bag of party favours is brought out —
bubbles, balloons, Bazooka gum.
Tell Beatrice thanks for the turtle.

Secret Potion

Take three dead flies off the window-sill
after they have been toasted
under a bright moon.
Dig a hole nine inches deep
under a birch tree
that leans due south.
Line the bottom and sides
with grey, flat stones
and say five times, 'Hydro'.
Find a green leaf that has fallen upside down.
Place on stones with point toward your heart.
Scatter sand into the magic hole
and arrange the flies
so they form a triangle.
Pluck a strand of hair
beside your right ear
and whisper, 'Oh hear me'.
Tie this strand of hair
around two small twigs
and place the bundle under the leaf.

Walk your fingers around the rim of the hole
until a ring appears in the mud.
On a black stone, scratch the picture
of a fish with the sun over it.
Hold this mystery between your hands
with your fingers locked
to form an envelope.
Breathe a warm breath into fish and sun
and place in the centre of the brittle fly triangle.
Your task is almost complete.
With the smallest handwriting
visible to the human eye,
explain your wish on paper
and, wrapping it in the petals of a flower,
drop it into the tunnel of earth
at midday exactly.

Meditation on Three Inches of Mud

I put my head to the mud one sunny day
and saw something green pushing its way up.
A worm disappeared
into the depths of the earth.
A beetle was messing around
with a lump of clay.
A little red bug was going
on the biggest adventure of his life
over the mountain-range of my knuckles.
I looked across at my own species
lolling on the grass
and tried to figure out
where we had taken the wrong turn.

Backyard Physics

'Look at this basketball:
Here we are up at the top.
And here are the Chinese
on the opposite side
or in other words at the bottom.
If you could see straight through
the earth under your feet
everything would be upside down.
But you wouldn't notice
because the gravity would stick you to the ground
to keep you from falling off. Just think,
all those Chinese living upside down
and they don't even care.
Aren't you glad we got stuck on the top?'

We looked at the ground under our feet.
We had never before understood
the hardships of being Chinese.

Chinese Giant

Poor Zeng Qin Lian.
She is the tallest woman in the world.
She is only sixteen and her father's head
is at her elbow.
Her bones ache when she stands —
she uses her family's shoulders for crutches.
She bends down every morning
to look at herself in the mirror.
It is not easy for her in China
where there is such an absence of height.
The neighbours point her out to visitors
as she is the only local landmark.
Her father noticed how difficult it was
for her to eat with normal chopsticks —
like slurping soup with a teaspoon.
He carved her a special set
as big as two candlesticks.
Now her six bowls of rice at lunch and dinner
don't take her so long to polish off.
I am sorry for you, Zeng Qin Lian.

A Sunny Day

The sun is shining
here in Ireland
so I decide to phone my mother
in America far away.
'Hi!', I say to her, 'it's me —
take out your sunglasses.'
She puts down the telephone
and gets a pair of shades.
'Are you there again?' I ask her.
'Now look outside at the sun: warm, right?'
She says, 'Yes, it's warm here,
the sun is beating down into this room.'
'Hey!' I say, 'it's on my hand
and on my knee, the same sunny day!'

Blur

A strange light
swirling with the steam from my bath:
was it row after row
of point shoes clicking
and net skirts shushing
as the mist comes rolling in
from both sides of the stage in Swan Lake?
Was it looking the sun
right in the eye on an August afternoon
with a fog horn
depressing all landlubbers?
Or was it sitting beside a steam radiator
in school watching a blizzard blow
through the crystal-patterned glass?
Through the blur I can almost see
my big toe turning on the hot water again.

Sun Reflections

I

I wish I were a sunbeam
dazzling the ripples on the water
sparkling on your hair
melting that kid's ice cream cone
shining in the window
jazzing up those tulips
dripping down a leaf
beaming gold toward a cloud

II

when I sit in the sun
wondering about a million stars
I've never seen
galaxies quasars pulsars
jewels dangling
in a black eternity
stretching my mind's
small human horizons
I laugh at my slightness
am secure
in the vastness
that encircles me
holds me
but cannot catch my thoughts

Polished Jade Stone

smooth in my palm
you fit so well
in the hollow of my hand
so well
into my eye socket
neatly
into the bottom of my neck
so cool against my cheek
deep in summer
where do you belong?

Surfboard Life

I'm riding on a surfboard life
someone gave me
a while ago I started out
in the middle of some wavy water
I've been surfing ever since
I fall off
a wave hits me from behind
then there I go
back on that surfing thing
I live on
no land is in sight
the streams of water
spray around me
I balance
the crest is below me
I can't be stopped now

Home

We will live some day
deep in a jungle
of grass and dandelion leaves —

travelling on a cricket
through twigs
rabbit holes and ant hills,

stopping to watch
a snake lose its skin
or a chrysalis become a butterfly.

In hot weather we'll ride a leaf
across a pond or take a
midnight journey on a firefly.

Our home will be wherever
we find warm earth
and a soft petal to sleep on.

Moving House

You sweat and swear
and yank and tug and lift
you fold you roll you press
you sweep you scrub you shine
until everything —
even the rubber band
at the back of the kitchen drawer —
is taken away.
Then you stare
at all the empty rooms
and don't look back.

TMPW—E

Two Paintings by Giuseppe Arcimbold

I   SPRING

She is a flower arrangement
hearing through a peony ear,
chewing with lily-of-the-valley teeth.

Dew falls on her carnation cheek,
sparkles in violet eyes.
She talks with rosebud lips.

II WINTER

He looks out of a crack in the bark:
a white mushroom mouth,
a bare head of stubs, vines and roots

waiting for warmth.
The moss on his neck is dead
and yellow — an old stubble.

He is a grey ghost
hiding in the forest — warty nose
more pale than cauliflower ear.

Mirror

A squirming, flapping
silver fish — our heads
crouch down near where
his eyes are open
on the cement.
We turn our gaze,
look up
to where he must be looking.
Near the clouds
flies a squirming, flapping
fish kite
someone has just caught.

1970

A man was screaming
a sports commentary
from under my pillow
as I leafed through *Seventeen*
hoping the multi-coloured drawing of a gym shoe
stuck to the ceiling
wouldn't fall down.
I didn't have to study history —
the answers were always neatly etched
on the desk tops by earlier classes.
In an hour my favourite T.V. show was on.
Hanging around my room
seemed the safest place to wait.

The Window and I

have spent our days together.
He is cold on the outside
and warm on the inside
like me.
We sit still
and listen to music in the afternoon.
He calls me over
when something is happening.
Even at night
when I've covered him up
I can see him breathing
and know he is watching
out for me.

Five Mysteries

One day, while passing down the hallway to the kitchen,
I noticed something strange opposite the cabinet
where we kept our good plates: three slightly curving steps
cut off by a piece of wood masquerading as a wall.
I mentioned this to my father
and asked him what they were for.
He said they were called the 'back stairs'
and that they went up to a little room we never used
and were covered over by a window seat.
He took off the board at the bottom
and we looked up the staircase.
Through the darkness and cobwebs a few rays of light
escaped from the hatch at the top.
They were the first mystery.

Beside the bathroom, on the second floor,
was a mirror with a handle;
if you grabbed and yanked, it opened.
In front of your face were shelves.
It was only when you leaned over and looked down
and felt the cold gust of air coming up at you
that you realised there was a long tunnel
leading into a place you couldn't see.
They said it was for dirty clothes —
to drop them down to the basement for washing.
We never threw our clothes down.
This was the second mystery.

The big bedroom had three bay windows
overlooking the street.
The walk-in closet had a diamond-paned window
with cut edges that made pins of rainbows on the walls.
Behind my mother's clothes was a secret cupboard
with her wedding dress and shoes
where she hid the Christmas presents.
Crammed into the corner, a glossy green dresser
hid a keyhole and a place for a doorknob
stuffed with newspaper.
I knocked. My brother answered.
'Who's doing that?'
'I am', I said. 'I'm in Mother's closet.
It's got a door. Where are you?'
He said, 'Cut it out,
I'm in my bedroom, of course.'
That door was the third mystery.

Down ten steps into the basement
in the middle of painted bricks
was a square trap door
which you were to crawl into
if a tornado came.
It was tunnelled out to the escape exit
under the front porch.
It was the fourth mystery.

They had been working in the attic
on our television aerial.
One of them said, 'There's something funny
about the third floor of this house.
It doesn't seem big enough.'
They poked around, pounding on the walls
until they found what they were looking for.
'Listen, it's hollow. That wall is just nailed in, see?
We'll get to the root of this!'
He pulled out the nails, tipped the wall
and it fell in.
We saw a bathtub standing on eagle's feet, a wagon whe
boxes, newspapers, junk. Our hair stood on end.
The fifth insoluble mystery.

74

A Street

Its smoke was so dense
you could ride on it
above the snow-covered city.
When the wind stood still
or forgot to blow,
I dipped down near
chimney pots and telephone wires.
The birds flew by,
waving their wings at me.
I rode over narrow streets
with dirty brick houses and,
in the distance, I could see
other smoke gliders —
all of us hoping
no one else knew.

Minute Book

I will give each hour
a name
so that, when I'm dying,
I will look at them again,
point to some and smile
'that hour was my friend'

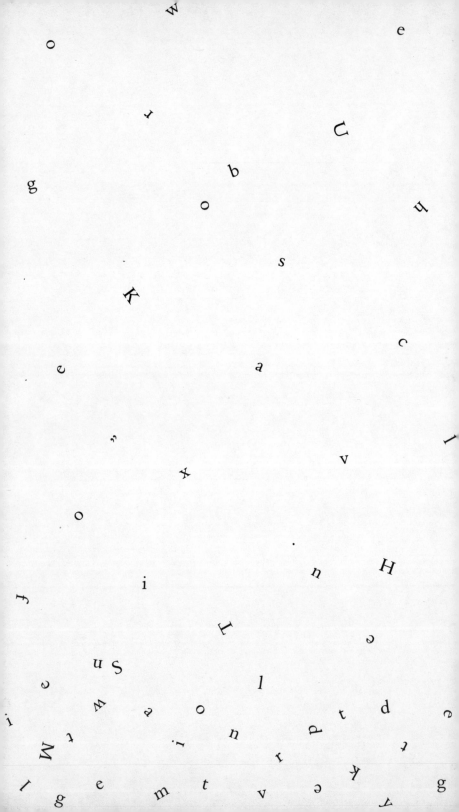